C000170556

Bernard Young is a professional writer
Yorkshire who leads writing workshops for children and adults. He has
given hundreds of performances in a variety of settings (from prisons to
pubs, leisure centres to libraries, as well as colleges, schools, playgroups
and supermarkets!). Bernard's poems have been broadcast on local and
national radio and feature in numerous anthologies of poetry for young
readers.

Tod Leedale was born in Bradford, spent his childhood abroad and decided
on a career in art and graphics because he could 'draw a bit'. He describes
himself as a childrens illustrator because that is mostly what he does and
what he enjoys most. Tod lives in Lincolnshire with girlfriend Wendy and
her two children and works in a small, cluttered back bedroom, mainly
producing graphics for an educational software company.

BRILLIANT!

Bernard Young

Illustrations by Tod Leedale

Kingston
Press

British Library Cataloguing in Publication Data.
A catalogue record for this book is available from the British Library.

First published 2000

All poems © 2000 Bernard Young
All illustrations © 2000 Tod Leedale

Published by Kingston Press

ISBN 1 902039 08 4

Kingston Press is the publishing imprint of Kingston upon Hull City Libraries, Central Library, Albion Street, Kingston upon Hull, England HU1 3TF
Telephone: +44 (0) 1482 616814
Fax: +44 (0) 1482 616827
E-mail: kingstonpress@hullcc.demon.co.uk
Internet: www.hullcc.gov.uk/kingstonpress

Printed by Kingston upon Hull City Council Printing Services, 1-5 Witham, Kingston upon Hull, England HU9 1DA.

KINGSTON UPON HULL   CITY COUNCIL

CONTENTS

BRILLIANT

Today Mum called me brilliant
and that's just how I feel

> I'll run a race
> i'm bound to win
> I'll take up golf
> Get a hole in one

Because today Mum called me brilliant
so that's what I must be

> I'll paint a picture
> A work of art
> I'll design a car
> It's sure to start

Because today Mum called me brilliant
and she always speaks the truth

> I'll write a song
> It'll be a hit
> I'll train a dog
> It'll stand and sit

Because today Mum called me brilliant
Yes, today Mum called me brilliant
Today Mum called me brilliant
So how am I feeling? BRILLIANT!

HERE COMES ANOTHER ONE OF DAD'S FAMOUS LAST WARNINGS

'I'm not going to
tell you
again,'

says Dad.

(Just before
he tells me
again).

GOOD FOR NOTHING

What's the point in being good for nothing?
Where's the reward in that!

Think I'll charge £5 an hour.
I'll grow rich and fat.

(£5 x 24 hours = £120 a day.
£120 a day, every day = £43,800 a year).

Well, it was worth a try
but Mum and Dad won't pay.

In fact, they say
they'll fine me

unless I am good
for nothing.

HALF ASLEEP

I roll out of bed
I'm half asleep

I slip on my slippers
I'm half asleep

I thump down the stairs
I'm half asleep

I slump at the table
I'm half asleep

I munch my cornflakes
I'm half asleep

I crunch my toast
I'm half asleep

I get up from the table
I'm half asleep

I slip (oops!) on my slippers
I'm half asleep

I fall on the floor
I'm half asleep

I fall asleep
Zzz …

A LIFE OF ADVENTURE

My bed
is a spaceship.

My pyjamas
are my spacesuit.

My bedroom is outer space.

When the light goes out
'we have lift-off.'

I hurtle towards planet sleep
and explore that world
until it is time to leave.

At first light
'we have touchdown.'

A safe landing.

I rise from my spaceship.
Rinse off the space dust.
Put on my earth clothes
and report to Mission Control.

I eat breakfast
and board the bus for school.

The school bus
is a submarine.

My school uniform
is a submarine commander's uniform.

The road I travel on
becomes the ocean I dive to the bottom of.

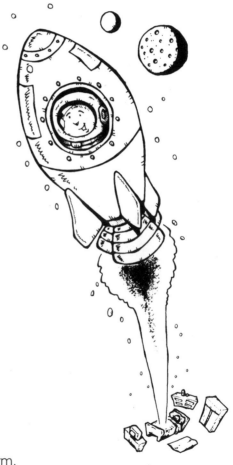

I'D LOVE TO DRIVE A TRACTOR

I'd love to drive a tractor
along a muddy track
and see the grooves its huge wheels leave
when, stopping, I look back.

I'd love to drive a tractor
along a narrow lane,
with a queue of cars behind me,
their horns being honked in vain.

I'd love to drive a tractor
across the school playground.
The teachers would come running out,
too surprised to make a sound.

One day I'll drive a tractor,
noisy, big, and green,
and you will see me coming
and I'll know where I've been.

ABSENT

Dear Teacher,
my body's arrived
it sits at a table
a pen in its hand
as if it is able
to think and to act
perhaps write down the answer
to the question you've asked

but don't let that fool you.

My mind is elsewhere.
My thoughts far away.

So apologies, teacher,
I'm not here today.

WHO

Trouble in the playground!
Bother in the class!
Who is there, in the midst of it?
I don't need to ask.

Who won't sit when told to sit?
Who won't stand up straight?
Who never puts his books away?
Who always turns up late?

Who put ink in the fish tank?
Who ate the hamster's food?
Who, when we have a guest in school,
Is the one who's always rude?

Haven't a clue?
I'll tell you.

You!
That's who!

It's true.

Whenever there's an outcry
And the Head says, 'I wonder who...'
I always know, don't ask me how,
That
    the
        person
            who
                is
                  you!

8

'WHAT ARE YOU DOING OUT HERE?'

Nice of you to ask, sir.
Thoughtful of you to think.
To even give me a glance, sir
Is a great encouragement.

Why I'm standing in the corridor?
That's what you want to know.
I've been sent out to cool my heels, sir
(Not that they were aglow).

I don't know exactly why, sir.
It might be because I was fighting
And I had a fit of the giggles
When I should have been quietly writing.

Oh...I did pull Jackie's hair, sir
But not really very hard
And she kicked me on the shin, sir
(A fact that's been ignored).

I'll see you after school, sir.
How kind of you to invite me.
Yes, we'll have one of our little chats, sir.
No, I don't take this matter lightly.

9

HERE COMES TROUBLE

I'm forever in trouble,
usually to blame,
so when they need a culprit
they always choose my name.

I know most staff and pupils
are sorry that I came
and since I did, I must admit,
things have never been the same.

To me it's not that serious;
a bit of fun, a laugh, a game.
It's just that when I see a target
I can't resist taking aim.

I spy a window that needs breaking,
a spotty first-year I can maim;
it's not exactly life and death
- shattered glass, a little pain.

They'll end up getting rid of me.
'He's no good!' they'll proclaim.
But being a nuisance gets me noticed.
Being bad's my claim to fame.

It's true: within the confines of the classroom
I have achieved a sort of fame;
I'm The Wild One, The Rebel,
the kid they cannot tame.

When they do expel me
I'll hang my head, as if ashamed,
but they'll know who's responsible
when the school goes up in flames.

ASHES TO ASHES

Here lies Tim, an inveterate liar.
Once too often he cried, 'Fire!'
The Firemen thought it was another lie
and left him to it - which is why
Tim's charred remains here do lie.

Moral: Kids who lie expire.

BRIGGSY

It's her birthday.
She doesn't want anyone to know.
She's not intending to celebrate
hitting the big 4 0.

Yes today Mrs Briggs is forty.
You can't tell. It doesn't show.
(And even if you think it does
don't you dare say so).

Because TODAY MRS BRIGGS IS FORTY
and she doesn't want anyone to know.

Although,
when someone in class has a birthday
she announces it and makes a big fuss

so

we'd like to make a big fuss of Mrs Briggs.
We've written a poem for her.
(We're planning to perform it in assembly).

It goes like this:

Mrs Briggs you're forty
That's quite an age to reach

Mrs Briggs you're forty
Long may you teach

Mrs Briggs you're forty
You don't want a fuss

Mrs Briggs you're forty
Your secret's safe with us

CONGRATULATIONS MRS BRIGGS ON TURNING 40

It's called *Mrs Briggs You're Forty*
and we hope she likes it.

BE-BOP-A-LULA

Four of our teachers have formed
A POP GROUP!

Mr Holland is on keyboards
Miss Costello sings
Mr Clapton plays guitar
Mrs Collins bashes drums.

My dad says he saw them, once,
performing in a pub.
His opinion: Well, for a bunch of teachers,
they were really rather good.

Perhaps they'll make a record.
Have a hit
and then quit school?

Tour the world as superstars?
Become hip?
And rich? And cool!

Until then
they'll have to teach us
how to read and how to write.

Hang on
to their day jobs.
Perform their music late at night.

And during breaks
(if they're not
on playground duty).

Note: They still need a bass player.
Any volunteers?

(Be-Bop-A-Lula: a rock classic which provided legendary rock'n'roller
Gene Vincent with his first million-seller in 1956).

KING BEE

I'm Bee Bee King,
King of Rhythm & Blues.
I play electric guitar ·
and wear blue suede shoes.

Give me a buzz
and I'll come and perform.
I'll fly straight over
with the rest of the swarm.

We'll bring Queenie.
She sings so sweet.
She'll soon have you humming
and tapping your feet.

The Sting:
If you like what you hear
I'll tell you what, honey,
don't say a word
just give us your money.

THREE NOTES CONCERNING A SQUASHED INSECT

C Ab B

THE BEDBUGS ARE THROWING A PARTY

The bedbugs are throwing a party
And I know who they're going to invite.
So select your best pyjamas
And arrange to stay the night.

You'll be their guest of honour.
The cause of great delight.
If you grace them with your presence
Everything will be just right.

Do accept their invitation
(To refuse would be impolite).
And please be there for the midnight feast –
It's you they're intending to bite!

RSVP to The Bedbugs, The Bed, Your Bedroom.

MY CROCODILE, MY SON

What a jolly croc you are
So charming and so jocular
Teeth a bit like Dracula
Don't forget to floss

What a solid rock you are
A chip off the old block you are
No wonder you're so popular
I've never seen you cross

But if anyone should mock you dear
Give them a big shock, my dear
Just you run amok, my dear
And show them who's the boss

Cause a little fear, my dear
Get a bit too near, my dear
Nip them on the rear, my dear
Have yourself some fun

Then be a jolly croc once more
So charming and so jocular
Sought after and popular
My crocodile, My son

VET REQUIRED: APPLY WITHIN

My pet is a monster,
a monster is my pet
and one day I decided
that he should see the vet.

The vet said, 'What's the problem,
is he off his food?'
I said, 'No, his appetite is monstrous,
mega, amazing, you'd...'

'Open wide,' said the vet.

'...be shocked at what he guzzles;
cardboard, carpets, cassettes.
He eats absolutely everything,
even...oh dear...vets!'

LIAM THE LIMPET

He was being a wimp
(At the end of his tether).
He was feeling limp
(Under the weather).
He needed to get a grip
if he was to pull himself together.

He'd had enough
(He couldn't hold on).
The sea was rough
(He wasn't strong).
He had to get a grip
if he was to survive in the ocean.

Liam was a worried limpet
(He didn't know what to do)
so he went to see the sea vet
who said, 'What I'll prescribe for you,
is a course in positive thinking
and a tube of superglue.'

Now Liam is far more impressive
(He never comes unstuck)
and he wants the whole wide world to know
about his positive new outlook.
(Which is why this poem needed writing
and sticking in a book).

ICEFISH

I'm not warm and cuddly.
I don't curl up on knees.
I don't pretend to be friendly.
I won't put you at your ease.

But I will give you the sniffles.
I will make you sneeze.
You'll find your chest will tighten
and you will start to wheeze.

'This icefish is not a nice fish'
you must, by now, be thinking.
'He's a bounder, he's a rotter,
he's a carrier of disease.'

But I do have a couple of good points, namely, these:
1. I won't poo on your carpet
2. I don't have fleas

However, I don't want to be your pet
and, please,
don't try to catch or eat me.

If you put me on a plate,
served up with chips and peas
you will get a nasty shock
- I taste of antifreeze!

(The icefish can survive in temperatures just below freezing. A fluid
similar to antifreeze in its blood makes this possible.)

IF I COULD PUT THE CLOCK BACK I WOULD

If you rely on
a lion
to tell you
the time
you might not
arrive on
the dot.

My one
was supposed to
ROAR
every half hour
but most
of the time
he forgot.

Now I've a clock
with a face
that shows me
the time
and it's always
precise
it's spot-on.

But oh why
did I buy one
I've upset
my lion
and my
forgetful old lion
has gone.

BIRDS OF A FEATHER

My cat
is old. All she
wants is food, warmth and a
comfy knee. My cat's a home bird.
Like me.

SANTA CLAUS AIN'T COMING ROUND NO MORE

Kids have sent me letters
But I ain't coming round

Mums are humming carols
But I ain't coming round

Everyone's expecting presents
But I ain't coming round

I've had enough
I'm getting old
My stiff joints ache
I feel the cold

So I ain't coming round!

But I am sending Santa Claus Junior.
He's taking over from me.

He might get your parcels muddled
or bump into your tree
(it will be his first year in the job)
so don't worry if you hear strange noises
if you cannot place a sound

It'll just be Santa Claus Junior
Cos I ain't coming
No, I ain't coming
I ain't coming
round!

WHAT DID YOU GET FOR CHRISTMAS?
(A SOB STORY)

I got a massive box of chocolates
But I didn't get a bike

I got some extra-special roller-skates
But I didn't get a bike

I got a mind-blowing computer game
But I didn't get a bike

I got two books and a bookmark
But I didn't get a bike

I got far more than I asked for
And not one gift that I dislike

But I'd hurl them in the river
I'd set them all on fire

I'd return each one to sender
If I could have a bike

It's not that I'm ungrateful
And I'm not usually impolite

But on Christmas Day my dream was
To ride and ride and ride

Instead, I crawled into a corner
And cried and cried and cried

All because I didn't (SOB)
I (SOB) didn't (SOB) get a (SOB) bike!

Maybe next year?

(SOB!)

I CAN SEE A GRUMPY FACE

I can see a grumpy face.
It isn't very pleasant.

It's not the sort of face
I'd give to anyone
as a present.

I'd like to put it
in a rocket
and send it into outer space.

Leave it up there
to grimace
and glower for several hours.

But I wouldn't want
that grumpy old face
to put all the stars out
and turn the moon sour

so I'd cut short
its high altitude interlude
and bring it back
to earth.

Perhaps, by then,
its bad mood
would have cleared off.

It's either that or

stop looking in the mirror.

NEW RULES, O.K.

If you're feeling glum
you must eat scrambled egg,
stand on one leg
and smile at your mum.

If you're feeling cross
you must drink lemonade,
get weighed
and pretend you're an albatross.

If you're feeling mean
you must eat an apple,
explore a castle
and paint your face green.

If you're being a pain
you must eat boiled rice,
think twice
and promise never to be one again.

I WISH I WAS A ROBOT

When robots are fighting
they don't feel pain.
They bash one another
again and again.

They clang when they clash.
They rattle and crunch.
Have head-on collisions
and don't stop for lunch.

I wish I was like them
then *I'd* suffer no pain
when punched and kicked
and punched again.

If I was a robot
I could cope with a lot.
If I was a robot.
But, sadly, I'm not.

SAFETY IN NUMBERS (COUNT ME IN)

I don't seek the limelight
Don't stand centre-stage
I look and I act
Just like my mates

    I'm part of the gang
    One of the crowd
    Safe in the knowledge
    That I don't stand out

Brave in a group
Proud to belong
Surrounded by friends
I feel big and strong

    It's great to be in
    I'd hate to be out
    I'm part of the gang
    One of the crowd

Perhaps when I'm older
I won't need an army
Of identical pals
Gathered around me?

But right now...

    I'm part of the gang
    One of the crowd
    Secure in the knowledge
    That I don't stand out

BORED

I'm kicking a ball
I'm kicking a ball
I'm kicking a ball against a wall

I'm bored
I'm bored
I'm bored   I'm bored   I'm bored

I'm banging my head
I'm banging my head
I'm banging my head against a wall

Hey! there are some girls
Hey! there are some girls
Hey! look over there   (where ?)
There are some girls

I'm dribbling the ball
I'm heading the ball
I'm bouncing the ball back off the wall

I'm cool
I'm cool
I'm cool I'm cool I'm cool

Hey! there go the girls
Hey! there go the girls
Hey! there go the girls
The girls have gone

I'm kicking a ball

I'm banging my head

I'm bored I'm bored I'm bored

ORANGE SOCKS

Orange socks
Orange socks
I've seen a girl wearing orange socks

Not blue not black
Not violet not pink

Orange socks
they make me think

of red hot days
the sun up above
when you don't need your scarf
you don't need your gloves

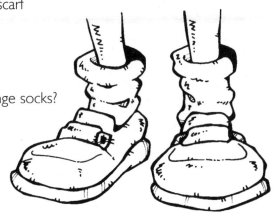

Orange socks
Orange socks
Who's that girl wearing orange socks?

Not brown not grey
Not yellow not green

But the orangiest orange
that I've ever seen

Orange socks
I like the style
Orange socks
They make me smile

Orange socks
Orange socks
Glad I saw that girl in those orange socks

GLUM & GLARY

I know a girl.
Her name is Mary.
Mary is big.
Mary is scary.

Her face is a picture
that's far from cheery.
Her mood is black
and doesn't vary.

'At a funny age.'
Glum and glary.
'Going through a phase.'
That's the theory.

I said to her Mum:
'Don't let her come near me.
Mary's so big.
Mary's so scary.'

But here she is.
Mean and bad.
She's looking for me.
Yeah, she wants...her...

'DAD!'

'HELP!'

ON SUNDAY I SLURPED

On Sunday I slurped superb soup
and got told off for slurping.

On Monday I munched mouthfuls of Maltesers
and couldn't eat my tea.

On Tuesday I tucked into turkey
and flicked sprouts at my brother.

On Wednesday I went without.
I was in trouble.

On Thursday I said 'No thank you'
to prove that I could go without.

On Friday I was famished and forced down
fish fingers, chips, peas, bread, egg custard, ice cream, arctic roll ...

On Saturday it was sandwiches
in front of the telly.

On Sunday I slurped superb soup
and got told off.

WHEN TO TEASE YOUR SISTER

Tease her on Monday
She'll go mad

Tease her on Tuesday
She'll be sad

Tease her on Wednesday
She'll give you a clout

Tease her on Thursday
She'll pull your teeth out

Tease her on Friday
She won't care

Tease her on Saturday
She'll wave her fists in the air

But tease her on Sunday
Without okaying it first
And your head will inflate
(Like a balloon)
And then BURST!

THE AGONY AUNTS

Don't mess with crazy Aunt Maisie
Don't upset her in any waysie
If you do she'll spring
(Boiling alive is her thing!)
But she's harmless compared to Aunt Daisy

CRIMINAL

I'm a one man walking crime wave
Nothing you've got is safe
Not your car Not your house Not your money
Not your dreams Not your life Not your grave

He's crooked
Proud of it

The crime rate soars
Goes through the roof
And I'm responsible
That's the truth

He's a villain
Makes a killing

No job too big
No job too small
I'll pick a pocket
I'll make a haul

Does his sums
Takes what comes

I'm a solo act
I'm the gang
I'm the brains behind
I drive the van

Versatile
Makes a pile

I know I'm guilty
But I feel no guilt
I won't worry
Till my collar's felt

He's hard
No heart

But getting caught
Is part of the game
So I keep schtum
I don't complain

Locked up
Shut away

Yes I'm inside
For a very long time
Lost my freedom
The fault's all mine

May I
Tell you why

He was a one man walking crime wave
Nothing you'd got was safe
Not your car Not your house Not your money
Not your dreams Not your life Not your grave

Shut up

Locked away

Shut up

Locked away

I'll be out
One day

Shut up!

HARD

Body kept in shape.
Body to be proud of.
Fit. Hard. Body
in its prime.

Body kept in shape.
Light on its feet.
See it run.
Punishing itself.

Body kept in shape.
Oblivious to cold.
Heat. Light-fingered.
Watch it.

Body kept in shape.
Lithe. Neat. Catch
it. Red-handed.
Punish it.

Body kept in shape.
Body kept in.
Body in its prime.
Doing time.

ROBOT WARS

The robots are fighting.
They don't feel pain.
They bash one another
again and again.

> Robots are tough
> Robots are mean
> Robot Wars!
> Don't intervene

They clang when they clash.
They rattle and crunch.
Have head-on collisions
and don't stop for lunch.

> Robots are tough
> Robots are mean
> Robot Wars!
> Machine v. Machine

But now there's just silence.
Not a robot in sight.
This is what happens
when robots fight.

> Robots are crazy
> Robots are daft
> Robot Wars!
> Not one robot left

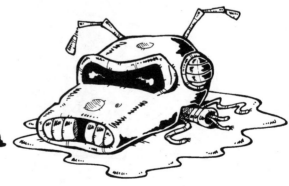

CAREER OPPORTUNITY: KNIGHT REQUIRED

Are you brave, honourable
and chivalrous?
Do you like wearing metal suits
and enjoy being called Sir?
Then this could be the job for you.

Your duties will include
wielding a sword, jousting
and clanking about.

Preference will be given
to those candidates
who come equipped
with their own warhorse and squire.

If you think
you've got what it takes
turn up for an interview
and show us what you can do.

NB Candidates will be left to fight it out amongst themselves.
Castle Management accepts no responsibility for loss of life or limb.

HORRIBLE POEM

Are you nasty
smelly
disgusting
one
to whom
all horribleness clings?
If you are
then I'm so glad
to meet you
because
I HATE NICE THINGS!

THE UGLIES

The Uglies are a funny breed.
They can't whistle. They can't read.
And, furthermore, you need to know this –
they have bad breath and pick their noses.

YOU'VE GOT TO HAND IT TO HIM

Michael's got a finger
halfway up his nose.
He's got a shoe and sock off
and is fiddling with his toes.
(If he had a third hand
what he'd do with it goodness knows).

But Michael comes in handy
when we've had enough of work.
He's our not-so-secret weapon
when we want to shirk.

Michael is, we're all agreed, a most disgusting lad.
All his personal habits are best described as bad.
You'll know how he acquired them
once you've met his Dad.
(Anyone who shakes *his* hand
must be raving mad).

His Mum, on the other hand,
seems slightly more refined.
She doesn't pick her nose or toes
or scratch at her behind.
(To mention her body odour here
would, I suppose, be unkind).

But her Michael comes in handy
when we've had enough of work
He's our not-so-secret weapon
when we want to shirk.

Michael is a dab hand
at making folk feel queasy.
If he lifts a finger
Teacher looks uneasy.
And once he's done his stuff
Teacher isn't bright and breezy.

'You must excuse me, class,' he groans.
'Please continue on your own.
I need a breath of fresh air
and twenty minutes all alone.'
Then he crawls out of the classroom
with a whimper and a moan.

Michael is, we're all agreed, a most disgusting lad.
All his personal habits are best described as bad
but he's the most effective pupil this class has ever had.

For Michael comes in handy
when we've had enough of work.
He's our not-so-secret weapon
when we want to shirk.

THE GREEN FINGER RAP

Some fingers do the walking
Some fingers point the way
Some fingers say come here
And some say go away

Some fingers they get angry
Some fingers they are rude
Some fingers say be quiet
Some fingers just get crude

Fingers, digits, pinkies
You all know what I mean
But tell me, have you ever seen
(And I'm not talking gan-ger-reen)
Fingers that are really green?

Well...I got green green fingers
I got green green fingers
I got green green fingers
I got fingers that are green

I can pot a plant
I can make it grow
I can dig and weed
I can reap and sow

I got green green fingers
I got fingers that are green

I can trim a hedge
I can prune a rose
I can set my veg
In nice neat rows

I got green green fingers
I got fingers that are green

My lawn is green
My house is green
My pol-i-tics
Are turning green

I got green green fingers
I got green green fingers
I got green green fingers
GREEN FINGERS!

ALIENS ARE SENDING ME MESSAGES

Aliens are sending me messages
I'm getting instructions from outer space

Stop washing your hands
Your neck
Your face

Aliens are sending me messages
I'm getting instructions from outer space

Eat more chocolate
More ice cream
More cakes

Oh, I like the instructions I'm getting
These messages from outer space

But Mum says if I obey them
my teeth will rot
and I'll smell.

And Dad's convinced
it's a crafty plot
to end the human race.

STARTING WITH ME!

But, of course, it's not.
Those aliens seem like a sensible lot
and deserve nothing but praise.

And I'll tell you what:

as long as they keep sending me messages
(instructions from outer space)
I'll continue guzzling chocolate
and never ever wash my face!

ADDICT

I don't choose cheese or chicken
I don't touch marzipan
Chocolate's my addiction
I indulge whenever I can

I gobble it for breakfast
I guzzle it for tea
Chock-a-block with chocolate?
Send for me

I may not have my own teeth
I may be overweight
But as a chocolate- chewing-chomper
I'm not just good - I'm GREAT!

Please don't prohibit chocolate
Don't impose a chocolate ban
Cos I'm a chocoholic
A desperate dangerous man

And I need chocolate - NOW!

WHEN GREAT-GRANDMOTHER TAKES HER FALSE TEETH OUT

When Great-Grandmother takes
her false teeth out
we fear her rubbery grin.

When she unsticks
those two fat lips of hers
- what a cavern!
we're scared of falling in...

Deep down, in her stomach,
are all the extra-strong mints she's sucked
and the overcooked cabbage
and the sprouts and the occasional roast duck
and the spoonfuls of syrup she took
to ease that tickly cough
and the oceans of sweet milky tea
that she can't seem to get enough of;
and those little nips of rum she's partial to
were a puddle, then a pond, now a lake
and she has her very own Everest - a mountain
of biscuit and cream and cake;
and there's toast and marmalade and cornflakes
porridge and apples and plums
plus all the stuff we haven't thought of
swimming inside her tum.

So if we ever did fall down there
I don't see how we could escape
unless, by some unlikely luck,
she happened to regurgitate
the mints, the cabbage, the sprouts, the duck
the syrup, the tea, the rum
the biscuit, the cream, the cake, the toast
the marmalade, the cornflakes, the plums;
and the apples; and the porridge; plus
all the stuff we haven't thought of;
and, of course - last in, first out - US!

52

MY GRANDAD

My Grandad
is a maniac.

He uses
the wrong side
of the road.

He parks
where he shouldn't.

He never signals...

I sometimes think
he shouldn't be allowed out
on that skateboard.

FOOTBALL FEVER

I've caught football fever
Now I'm football mad
Football's taken over
I've got football bad

Yes, I've got football fever
I thought I was immune
But I'm not *sick as a parrot*
Instead I'm *over the moon*

So I don't need a doctor
I don't need a pill
I'm not feeling awful
I'm not really ill

I've just got football fever
I've just gone football mad
I'm as crazy as my sister
As barmy as my Dad

We've all got football fever
Each one did succumb
But if you think *we've* got it bad
Wait till you meet Mum!

MAKING A MEAL OF IT

What did you do at school today?

Played football.

Where are you going now?

To play football.

What time will you be back?

After football.

Football! Football! Football!
That's all I ever hear.

Well!

Well don't be late for tea.

O.K.

We're having football casserole.

Eh?

Followed by football crumble.

What?

Washed down with a...

As if I can't guess!

nice pot of...

I'm not listening!

tea.

THE START OF MY CAREER

I've been picked?
I've really been picked?
You mean I've been picked for the football team?

Pinch me hard.
Wake me up.
Can this be a dream?

No dream!

You've been picked.
You've really been picked.
You have been picked for the football team.

You're the substitute's substitute's substitute
so you'll probably not
get a game.

But we need to know you're ready.
Able. Willing. Keen.
The second eleven might need you.
Come running if we call your name.

Because you've been picked.
You've really been picked.
You have been picked for the football team.

Wow!

Iron my kit.
Polish my boots.
I'm the substitute's substitute's substitute.

The substitute's substitute's substitute:
I'll probably not
get a game.
The substitute's substitute's substitute:
I'm honoured
all the same.

I'm usually ignored.

But now
I've been picked

I've sort of
been picked

I've almost
been picked

For the Football Team.

(It's a start).

REF RAP

Clap clap
Clap clap clap
Clap clap clap clap
Clap clap

I don't win
I don't lose
I point the finger
Uphold the rules

I show the card
I send them off
I blow the whistle
When I've had enough

Clap clap
Clap clap clap
Clap clap clap clap
Clap clap

Fans all chant
Supporters sing
Can't hear the words
I like to think
It's

'We love
We all love
We all love the referee'

Clap clap
Clap clap clap
Clap clap clap clap
Clap clap

'He's brave
He's strong
His eyesight's great
He's not the man
We love to hate

He does no wrong
He's always right
He's on the ball
He's dynamite

And we love
We all love
We all love the referee'

Clap clap
Clap clap clap
Clap clap clap clap
Clap clap

I don't get dirty
I don't get hurt
In my referee's shorts
In my referee's shirt

It's plain to see
So you must agree
The man to be
Is the referee

Ref ref
Ref ref ref
Ref ref ref ref
Ref ref

ACKNOWLEDGMENTS

The author's poems were first published as indicated:

Absent, *Excuses, Excuses*, O.U.P. 1997
Aliens Are Sending Me Messages, *We Are Not Alone*, Macmillan 1999
Be-Bop-A-Lula, *The Secret Lives of Teachers*, Macmillan 1996
Birds of a Feather, *Poetry Poster*, Folens 2000
Bored, *Doin Mi Ed In*, Macmillan 1993
Briggsy, *More Secret Lives of Teachers*, Macmillan 1997
Career Opportunity, *Hysterical Historical Poems - Middle Ages*, Macmillan 2000
Good for Nothing, *Custard Pie*, Macmillan 1996
Hard, *Criminal Records*, Viking 1994
Here Comes Another One of Dad's Famous Last Warnings, *Parent-Free Zone*, Macmillan
Making a Meal Of It, *We Was Robbed*, Macmillan 1997
My Grandad, *Penny Whistle Pete*, Collins 1995
Ref Rap, *'Ere We Go*, Macmillan 1993
Safety In Numbers, *My Gang*, Macmillan 1999
The Bedbugs Are Throwing A Party, *Minibeasts*, Macmillan 1999
The Start of My Career, *They Think It's All Over*, Macmillan 1998
Three Notes Concerning a Squashed Insect, *My First Has Gone Bonkers*, Blackie 1993
What Are You Doing Out Here?, *Excuses, Excuses*, O.U.P. 1997
When Great Grandmother Takes Her False Teeth Out, *Revenge of the Man-Eating Gerbils*, Macmillan 1999

The following poems were published in *Double Talk*, Stonecreek Press 1994/Eastwords 1998: Bored, Hard, Orange Socks, Ref Rap, The Green Finger Rap, Three Notes Concerning a Squashed Insect.